HELP!

MY CARS & TRUCKS
HAVE **DRIVEN AW**

I had **cars & trucks**, but now I have **none**...

I left the gate open; now they've all **gone!**

Forgive me for such a silly blunder... where could they be, i wonder?

SCREECH & BEEP

I put these in my garage,
then I locked the door...

but when i checked this morning,
they weren't there anymore!

ZULU & TANKER

I've **lost the trucks**,
but I've **still got the keys**.

Help me find them; pretty please!?

One is for my **sister**, and the other is for **me**. I can't find them; **where could they be?**

BERTHA & BRUNO

Work is about to stop for the day.
Can you spot these two
before they **drive away**?

HONKLE & GRAMPS

These cars are old, and really quite **slow**. I'd still love you to **find them though!**

CHUCKY & FOGGLE

One is orange, and the other is white. I'd love to see them, but they've **vanished out of sight!**

DUCKY & VIOLET

Losing these two has made me **quite sad**.

If you find them for me, I'll be **super glad**!

HORNET & SAPPHIRE

One is lovely shade of green, while the other is blue...

I wonder where they've **gotten to?**

SPARKY & SWISH

I bought these last month;
they're really quite new.

Where could they be?
I haven't got a clue!

BLINK & BOLT

Both cars are fast,
if you take them for a spin.
If they had a race,
I'm not sure who would win!

DUNKY & BARKY

These trucks serve the **best**
donuts and hot dogs around.
But, i wonder, can they be **found**?

TANG & RIBBIT

These two cars
have driven away.
Where are they now?
I hope they're OK!

ROLLO & SLINGER

New roads are being built,
and my trucks have worked all week.

I'd like them back now though,
but they're **playing hide and seek!**

WAVE & BUMPY

Find these two,
if you'd **be so kind**.

These two are the
last two to find!

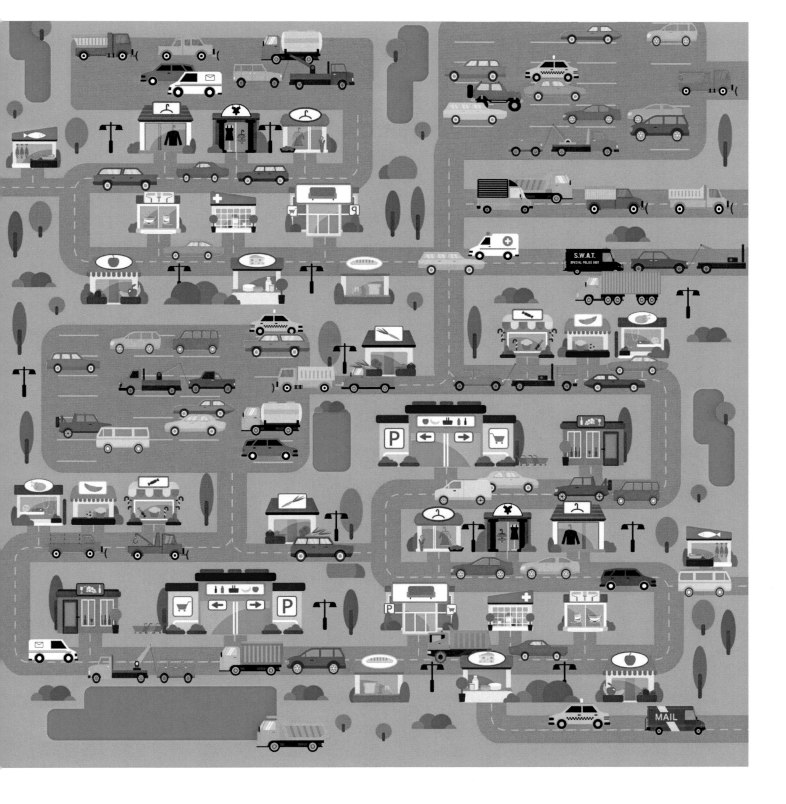

THANK YOU!

They've all been found...

and here they are,

all safe and sound!

A bonus search!

PLANE SPOTTING!

The three above are hiding in the book. Don't believe me? Go take a look!

THE END!

NEW to Amazon

Type the unique number in the Amazon search bar... **and it'll take you right to it!**

1914047052

1914047060

1914047079

1914047117

B096X7H7P4

1914047087

BESTSELLERS!

Type the unique number in the Amazon search bar... **and it'll take you right to it!**

1980596743

1973102145

1728837782

1976776511

1724117491

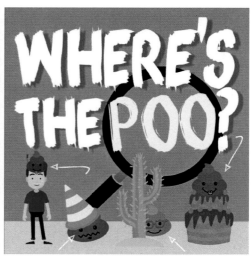

1549977660

Made in United States
North Haven, CT
14 March 2022

17160939R00022